AIRCRAFT
MADE IN
LINCOLN

Dedication

THIS BOOK IS INTENDED AS A MEMORIAL TO THE MEN AND WOMEN

ENGAGED IN AIRCRAFT WORK IN LINCOLN IN THE TWO WORLD WARS.

THE NAMES OF THE GREAT ENGINEERING COMPANIES OF THESE PAGES

HAVE ALL DISAPPEARED, BUT THE SPIRIT OF PAST GLORIES LIVES ON.

Published by The Society for Lincolnshire History and Archaeology

Jews' Court, Steep Hill, Lincoln LN2 1LS

© The Society for Lincolnshire History and Archaeology

Text copyright © John Walls and Charles Parker

First published 2000

ISBN 0 903582 16 3

British Library Cataloguing in Publication Data

A CIP catalogue record for this book is available from the British Library

The publishers and authors gratefully acknowledge the grant made by the
"Millennium Festival Awards For All" Fund towards the cost of producing this book.

Supported by the
Heritage Lottery Fund

Printed in Great Britain by J.W. Ruddock & Sons Ltd., Lincoln

CONTENTS

NOTES ON SOURCE MATERIAL
AND ACKNOWLEDGEMENTS

This book is based on the series of three Lincolnshire Aircraft Production booklets by John Walls published between 1974 and 1977.

The sections on Avro Aircraft Repair and the Aircraft Acceptance Parks have been compiled by Charles Parker, who has also followed up many leads in Lincoln.

The Ruston Archive tended by Ray Hooley has provided all of the Ruston material. The 1918 'Ruston Aircraft Production' and 1919 'Our Part in the Great War' books provided an excellent account of the Great War output. The Abell collection in Lincoln Library provided material for the airfield section. The History of the Ministry of Munitions in the IWM library detailed the National Aircraft Factory proposals.

One Ruston and two Clayton aircraft survive. One or two propellers and other parts still exist. A small number of drawings and glass plates have also survived.

Many of the Great War pictures were the work of two Lincoln photographers Mr Walker and Mr Harrison. Walker's Studio, now part of the Grand Hotel can be seen in the 'Seaplane in the Station Yard' photograph. The photographs have been restored by Liisa Hilden-Parsons. Other photographs are from the J.M. Bruce / G.S. Leslie collection, Chaz Bowyer and the Lincolnshire Echo. Thanks also to Neville Franklin for the aircraft drawings and Tony Hancock for the airfield plans. The munitions factories map is after Peacock Wright & Turner. For additional material and help our thanks to Jim Halley of Air Britain, Barry Abraham and John Ainsworth of the Airfield Research Group, Neville Birch, Peter Stevenson, H.B. Clarricoates, Andrea Wright of Wyman-Gordon (Lincoln) Ltd, Chris Stevenson of Dalgety Agriculture, J.H. Thomason and Alf Webster. Roger Audis supplied information about the On War Work badges.

JOHN WALLS
Leicester 2000

CHARLES PARKER
Lincoln 2000

LINCOLN
AND THE GREAT WAR

"THIS IS AN ENGINEERS' WAR"

David Lloyd George at Bangor, February 28th 1915

LINCOLN IS USUALLY REMEMBERED AS THE BIRTHPLACE OF THE TANK AND IT IS NOT OFTEN REALISED THAT AT THE TIME OF THE GREAT WAR, THE CITY WAS ONE OF THE LARGEST AIRCRAFT PRODUCTION CENTRES IN THE WORLD. RUSTON, PROCTOR & CO. LTD WAS THE FIRST LINCOLN FIRM TO VENTURE INTO AIRCRAFT PRODUCTION, IN RESPONSE TO A GENERAL CALL FOR A GREATER DIVERSION OF THE ENGINEERING INDUSTRY INTO AERONAUTICAL WORK. LATER ROBEY & CO. LTD AND CLAYTON & SHUTTLEWORTH LTD MOVED INTO AIRCRAFT PRODUCTION. SMALLER COMPANIES WERE ALSO INVOLVED IN SUBCONTRACT WORK. AROUND 6,000 MEN AND WOMEN WERE 'ON WAR SERVICE' ON AIRCRAFT WORK IN THE CITY. ONE IN FOURTEEN BRITISH AIRCRAFT OF THE GREAT WAR WAS MADE IN LINCOLN.

A HUGE AMOUNT OF OTHER MILITARY HARDWARE WAS ALSO PRODUCED IN LINCOLN FACTORIES INCLUDING MARINE ENGINES, MINES, PARAVANES, BUOYS, BOILERS, HORSE SHOES, SHELLS, FLAME PROJECTORS, LETHAL GAS APPARATUS, GUN MOUNTINGS AND CATERPILLAR TRACTORS - THE FORERUNNER OF THE TANK.

RUSTON PROCTOR & Co. LTD

IN 1857 JOSEPH RUSTON BECAME A PARTNER IN THE SMALL LINCOLN MILLWRIGHTS BUSINESS OF BURTON & PROCTOR. THE COMPANY BECAME RUSTON, PROCTOR & CO. LTD AND SOON EXPANDED. IN 1914 THE WORKS COVERED 100 ACRES, WITH OVER 5,000 EMPLOYEES.

On January 15th, 1915, one hundred B.E.2c aircraft were ordered and, from this small beginning, Rustons expanded to become the largest producer in the country of aircraft engines, and came amongst the leading five British aircraft constructors of the Great War for aircraft output. Over 2,000 aircraft were built by the company and production of aero engines exceeded 3,000 units with a further quantity equivalent to 800 engines delivered as spares. At the end of the war about three thousand men and women were employed on aeronautical work at Rustons.

THE B.E.2c

Ruston's first type of aeroplane was developed from a 1911 design, by F. M. Green and Geoffrey de Havilland of the Royal Aircraft Factory, Farnborough, for a two seat tractor biplane.

⊙ *The first Ruston aeroplane to be test flown at Lincoln, BE2c 2671*

The early Factory B.E.2 machines were developed by a young engineer, Edward Busk, into the inherently stable B.E.2c machine of June 1914. Stability was then deemed to be a most desirable quality for a reconnaissance and gun platform aircraft. However, this was to prove the machine's undoing in France where the B.E. was easy prey for enemy scouts. The original B.E.2c powerplant, a 70 h.p. Renault engine, had been replaced by the 90 h.p. R.A.F. Ia engine (a development of the Renault) when Rustons started to build the machine. New buildings were quickly erected in Lincoln on waste ground bordering the River Witham at Boultham and at Spike Island. The first B.E.2c machine, number 2670, was completed exactly six months after the placing of the order and was taken by rail to Farnborough for testing.

The second B.E.2c was test flown at Lincoln by Captain Tennant making an initial half hour flight watched anxiously by Ruston's directors. Alex Ramsay, the aircraft department manager at Rustons, was later taken up for a flight in the machine. This aircraft, number 2671, was delivered to Farnborough by air on the 18th July, 1915. Tennant, accompanied by Mr. W. B. Feasey of Rustons as a passenger, left the West Common and followed the railway line for London. However, the pair lost their way and landed in a field near Sandy in Bedfordshire. The aviators lunched with a local farmer before setting course for Hendon and tea, finally arriving at Farnborough at 7 p.m.

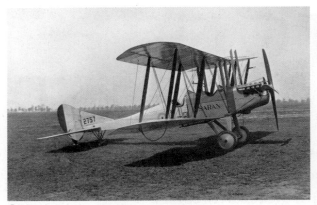

BE2c 2757 Saran, note later style vertical exhaust

The first Ruston built BE2c 2670 in the erection shop

Harold D. Boultbee, who later became quite well known in the field of aircraft design, then head of Ruston's aeronautical department drawing office was also taken up in an early B.E.2c, number 2682.

The fourth B.E.2c to be built, 2673, was used by Lieutenant W. Leefe Robinson to down the first German rigid airship on British soil at Cuffley, Herts. on September 3rd, 1916. For this feat, Robinson was awarded the Victoria Cross.

At least two machines from the batch fell into German hands, 2742 and 2769, the latter as late as April 1917. Many famous pilots came to Lincoln to test fly Ruston B.E.2s including such names as Hucks, Pixton, Salmond and Semphill.

BE2c propeller at Culzean Castle, Ayrshire, note Ruston badge. The 'Zeppelin' was in fact Shutte-Lanz SL 11 (JW)

BE2c 2699 hanging in the Imperial War Museum in the 1960s. Rebuilt at Duxford in the early 1990s, it is now back at Lambeth in original natural finish (JW)

LATER B.E.2s

Rustons received a further order for a hundred B.E.2s. The first of these was delivered as a B.E.2d on the 20th April, 1916. Thirty-one aircraft were built as B.E.2ds, the remainder of the order being delivered as B.E.2es with short span lower wings. Production of the B.E.2e was completed early in 1917 by which time Rustons were building better war planes from the Sopwith stable.

⬆ BE2 wings being covered in the factory

⬆ Rolls Royce Hawk engine installation on a Ruston BE2e seen in the West Common aircraft sheds (RR)

⬆ BE2e 6259 with Rolls Royce engine

⊕ *Sopwith 1 1/2 Strutter in the factory*

THE SOPWITH 1 1/2 STRUTTER

The Sopwith was a two seat scout designed by Herbert Smith for the Admiralty late in 1915. The War Office, noting its superiority over their own B.E.2 machines, eventually ordered the aeroplane. Rustons became the first contractor to build the Sopwith 1 1/2 Strutter for the Royal Flying Corps.

The Sopwith was the first British scout to be fitted with a synchronized Vickers gun at the top of the fuselage, firing forward through the propeller arc. The first few Ruston built machines had the rather crude Nieuport overhead gun ring mounting the Lewis gun in the rear cockpit. Later machines in the first production batch were fitted with the Scarff No. 2 gun ring.

The 1 1/2 Strutter was powered by the nine cylinder 110 h.p. Clerget 9Z rotary engine, built by Rustons under licence from Gwynnes of Hammersmith and Chiswick, the U.K. concessionaires of the French Clerget-Blin Company. The first machine, 7762, force landed three miles from Peterborough on its delivery flight to Farnborough on the 11th July, 1916. It was finally tested at the Royal Aircraft Factory on the 20th of the month. The second Sopwith, 7763, served with 45 Squadron and was later captured by the Germans. In all, Rustons built four batches of the 1 1/2 Strutters, the last ones being built alongside the legendary Sopwith Camel. Some of these were powered by the 130 h.p. Clerget 9B engine, developed by W. O. Bentley from the earlier 9Z. The engine differed from the earlier Clergets with aluminium pistons. The last 1 1/2 Strutter, B2600, was delivered to Ascot on the 25th July, 1917.

⬆ *Sopwith 1½ Strutter production 7762 on the right*

⬆ *7762 ready for test flight*

⬆ *Sopwith 1½ Strutter 7777 note Nieuport gun mount*

↥ Camel B2312 at Farnborough 3.10.1918

↥ Churchill and Ruston Camel B2538

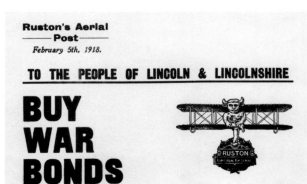

↥ War Bond leaflet as dropped from the 1000th aeroplane piloted by
Lieutenant J.H. Moore

↥ Sopwith Camel B2428 on final assembly

↥ B7380 Ruston's 1000th aeroplane

↥ B7380 and pilot (JMB/GSL)

↑ *Camel B7320 damaged by 'very heavy Archie fire on patrol over Hunland'*

THE SOPWITH CAMEL

The Sopwith Camel, conceived late in 1916, was Herbert Smith's answer to the latest German bid for air superiority, the Albatros biplane. Rustons became the first War Office contractor for the type when an order for two hundred and fifty was placed early in 1917. The first machine, B2301, was completed on 1st June, 1917 and flown to France via Lympne on the 14th June 1917. The Camel remained in production at Rustons until the end of November 1918 and the firm built 1,600 examples of the machine, more than any other builder.

↑ *Two seat Camel conversion B7371 (JMB/GSL)*

Most of the factory machines derived from a Sopwith-built pattern aircraft N6344, were equipped with various marks of the Ruston-built Clerget 9B rotary engine. Some machines were modified in service use to take different engines. Several Camels were converted into two seater machines at training bases.

On the 4th January, 1918 Rustons completed their 1000th aircraft, Camel B7380. By special permission, the machine was given a fantastic colour scheme, presumably instigated by Colonel Ruston himself, a keen Egyptologist. The Camel was emblazoned with the Behudet, an Egyptian winged sun, and was delivered for flying tests on the 25th January, 1918. B7380 was formally accepted by the Comptroller-General of Aircraft Equipment, Major-General W. Sefton Brancker, at a special ceremony on February 1st. On the 5th, the machine flew over Lincoln dropping 5,000 'Ruston's Aerial Post' leaflets advertising War Bond Week. This was so successful that it was decided to drop 10,000 per day during Lincoln War Bond Week, March 4th-9th, 1918.

Upon completion of the 1000th aeroplane, Major W.S. Brancker, Comptroller General of Equipment, Imperial Air Service, visited Ruston's aircraft factory to compliment the employees upon their energy and devotion to duty. The photograph was taken immediately after the speech

B7380 at a Red Cross day, Great Northern Station yard

⊕ D8185 fuselage being wheeled through the streets of Lincoln by a group of Ruston Munitionettes seen here at the Cattle Market. The occasion was a women's rally to recruit for the Land Army. Nationally, women made up one third of the munitions labour force in 1918

⊕ D1922 Siam No.2 presentation Camel (JMB/GSL)

⊕ E1548 Newton Abbot presentation Camel (JMB/GSL)

⬆ The propeller shop. Planks were cut to template shapes and laminated together. Spokeshaves were used to plane down to the joints to create the correct aerofoil. The blades were then balanced

The Kerr Pattern Co. in Rosemary Lane ➡
made propellers using a Ransome cutting
machine tracing from a pattern blade to
the right of the picture. They continued
propeller manufacture until 1930

⊕ *Clerget engine test shop*

⊕ *A group of engine workers*

⊕ *Clerget engine being test run*

⬆ *A Ruston built Bentley BR2 engine on centre pivot stand*

⬆ *A selection of Ruston built bombs. On the left 230lb HE RFC bomb, centre S.N. bomb, right S.N. Major bomb, length 14ft 7ins, weight filled nearly 1½ tons. Apparently called S.N. to bomb Essen. Rustons produced over 500,000 shells and bombs*

⬆ *ABC Dragonfly engine*

THE SOPWITH SNIPE

Ruston's last machine was Herbert Smith's replacement for the Camel, the 7F1 Snipe. The type was powered by Bentley's 230 h.p. BR2 engine, the first British production engine with aluminium cylinders, which was also built by Rustons. The first Snipe, E7337, was delivered in October 1918. Late production aircraft featured a revised tail fin and horn-balanced ailerons. Many Snipes, and indeed late production Camels, were put into storage and eventually scrapped. Quite a number of Ruston Snipes were reserved for Royal Air Force use post-war and, as late as 1924, sixty-eight were still in service.

Aircraft work at Rustons was slowly run down and replaced by motor car production. Snipes after E7798 (12/6/1919) were delivered to Oddfellow's Hall, Thetford, for finishing by the Portholme Aerodrome Company of Huntingdon. The final production batch of 300 Snipes was started. The first fourteen (H351 to H364) were delivered to Thetford between 28th August and 10th September, 1919. The next eleven (H365-375) were delivered without engines to Waddon, near Croydon, on September 17th. Aircraft work stopped at Rustons on the 20th September, 1919 when H449 had just been started. All of the aircraft in the works were dispatched to Thetford and Huntingdon, Rustons becoming an aircraft constructor of the past.

⊙ *Royal visit to the works of Ruston Proctor & Co. Ltd., April 9th 1918. Queen Mary and King George V in centre. A. Borneman and Col. J.S. Ruston J.P. at left, chairman, F. Howard Livens, Chief Engineer to the left of the King, and G.R. Sharpley, director to his right*

⊕ *Constructors plate Sopwith 7F1 Snipe (JW)*

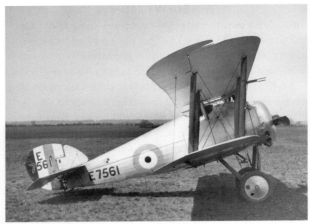

⊕ *Snipe E7651 at Stag Lane June 1925 (PT Capon)*

⊕ *Ruston built Sopwith Snipe E7370 on the West Common*

MISCELLANY

Ruston, Proctor & Co. Ltd became Ruston and Hornsby Ltd on the 11th September, 1918 following the merger with Richard Hornsby & Sons Ltd. of Grantham and J. E. H. Andrew & Co. Ltd. of Stockport. Aircraft and engines which were started after this date bore the Ruston & Hornsby manufacturer's plate and badges.

Besides aircraft and engines, Rustons produced a variety of other military hardware including 8,000 Lewis guns. In addition to the aircraft described they were involved in another project, a flying bomb, known for security reasons as an 'aerial target' which was designed at the Royal Aircraft Factory.

○ Ruston built carrier pigeon loft outside Lincoln Castle gates during War Bond Week. A Borneman, Ruston M.D. on the left and Master Gerald Ruston centre

○ Ruston built Sopwith Snipes stored at the Aircraft Disposal Co. hangar Waddon, Croydon

○ Aerial Target flying bomb

An engine-less example is depicted in the Ruston book 'Our Part In The Great War' but no records exist to substantiate whether or not the machine got beyond the mock-up stage.

Rustons built one other aero engine, the static 340 h.p. nine cylinder A.B.C. Dragonfly radial, designed by Granville Bradshaw. Eleven thousand were ordered while the engine was still in the development stage. The largest single order for the engine, a batch of 1,500 went to Rustons in 1918. The Dragonfly was never perfected and all contracts were cancelled soon after the end of the war.

Only one Ruston and Proctor aeroplane still survives, B.E.2c, 2699, with the Imperial War Museum, London. Newark Air Museum has a number of Ruston Snipe parts. Several Ruston-built Clergets are known to survive. In this country, a sectioned Ruston Clerget is exhibited at the Shuttleworth Collection at Old Warden, Bedfordshire, and at Hendon in the Royal Air Force Museum, the Camel, Sopwith Triplane and Avro 504K all have Ruston Clerget 9Bs as does the Science Museum's Avro 504K, currently on display at Middle Wallop. One Ruston engine BR2A No50131 was still flying in the Nieuport built Sopwith Snipe E6938 of Canadian National Aeronautical Collection in the 1960s.

ROBEY
& Co. LTD

EARLY IN 1915 ROBEY AND COMPANY LTD. BECAME THE SECOND LINCOLN FIRM TO MANUFACTURE AIRCRAFT FOR THE GREAT WAR. THE FIRM BUILT QUITE A VARIETY OF AIRCRAFT TYPES FOR THE ADMIRALTY UNTIL 1919. DESPITE THE FACT THAT THEIR OUTPUT WAS NOT AS GREAT AS THAT OF THE OTHER LINCOLN AIRCRAFT CONTRACTORS, RUSTON PROCTOR AND CLAYTON & SHUTTLEWORTH, THE ROBEY COMPANY WAS THE ONLY ONE IN THE AREA TO GO AS FAR AS DESIGNING AND BUILDING PROTOTYPES OF THEIR OWN MACHINES.

⬆ Sopwith Gunbus production in the Coultham Street aircraft works

THE SOPWITH GUNBUS

The first aeroplane type to be built by Robey and Company was the Sopwith type 806 Gunbus. New aircraft shops in Coultham Street were built by F. W. Horton Ltd. early in 1915. The aircraft were erected in the new shops and the mainplanes were covered and doped in a large wooden shed behind the main Canwick Road works.

Drawings of the Gunbus, the first Sopwith type to be sub-contracted, were prepared for Robeys by R. J. Ashford of the Sopwith Aviation Company, Kingston-upon-Thames, and these were approved by Herbert Smith, the designer of the machine, on 6th May, 1915. Contract CP51744115 to build the machines was issued by the Admiralty on 21st May, 1915.

The Robey built machines were fitted with 150 h.p. water cooled V-8 Sunbeam Nubian engine and were designed to carry two 65lb bombs under each lower wing when fully loaded. The machines were equipped with extra bomb racks to enable them to carry a total of six 65lb bombs with a reduction in the amount of petrol carried.

○ Sopwith Gunbus in flight over the West Common. Brickworks chimney in the background

The first machine, 3833, was completed during the summer and was flown on the race course by Sopwith's test pilot, Harry Hawker. Machine No.3839 was despatched to Sopwith's flight test centre at Brooklands, as was No.3834. On 30th September the first machine returned to Lincoln for replacement of its Sunbeam engine. Amongst the test pilots of these first Robey machines on the West Common racecourse was one William Francis Semphill, who later became Lord Semphill, in later years a member of Robey's board of directors.

The early machines had Union Jack markings on the rudder above the serial number; on later machines the rudder bore British red, white and blue stripes with the serial on the fin. The Sopwith pusher was not very successful and was quickly obsolete.

Only seventeen were completed, the last thirteen machines of the Robey batch being delivered as spares. Some of the machines were flown as trainers at Eastchurch and Hendon aerodromes by the Royal Naval Air Service. A Sopwith-built Gunbus, No.803, was repaired at the end of 1915.

○ The first machine 3833 ready for test. Left to right: Davis, Hawker, Peters, W.T. Bell, Robey M.D., Lt. C.R. Abbot and Lt. J.O. Nicholl

➊ *Gunbuses 3845 and 3846 at South Park en route to the airfield*

➊ *3833 being prepared for first flight*

⬆ *Robey Tractor Scout*

THE ROBEY SCOUTS

The Robey aircraft design department, under Mr. J. A. Peters, worked on two single seat scout designs in 1915. One of these, a smart tractor biplane, not unlike a Sopwith Tabloid, was built in the long wooden shed behind the works. Progress on the machine was hindered by the unavailability of a suitable rotary engine. On completion, the machine was despatched to Hendon aerodrome under the charge of two of the aircraft department foremen, Mr. Harmston and Mr. Dracup, to await delivery of an engine. The intended 80 h.p. Gnome rotary engine was not delivered and, after staying some time at the Welsh Harp near Hendon aerodrome, the pair returned to Lincoln with the tractor scout which was put into storage at the works.

The other machine, a pusher scout to be powered by either a 80 h.p. Gnome rotary or a 90 h.p. Salmson M7 water cooled radial engine, was not built.

⬆ *Tractor Scout with J.A. Peters in the cockpit*

⬆ *First Robey built Short 184, 9041*

THE SHORT 184 SEAPLANE

Robey's second aircraft order came in November 1915 when twenty Short type 184 Seaplanes were ordered by the Admiralty. The Short machine was widely sub-contracted, Robey & Co. being amongst the second group of sub-contractors for the seaplane and the firm continued to produce the design into 1919. Robeys built more of these machines than any other company, completing a total of 256 machines out of over 800 built and reaching a production rate of one per day. The machines were delivered by road to various seaplane bases for testing such as Inverkeithing in Fifeshire, Calshot near Southampton and Killingholme on the Humber.

The Short seaplane was the 'workhorse' of the Admiralty, flying in all naval theatres of war from seaplane stations and seaplane carriers. The machines were generally powered by variants of the Louis Coatalen designed Sunbeam engine. These engines had little used names. The variants of the 12 cylinder V-engine used in Robey Short 184s were:

225 h.p. Sunbeam Mohawk

240 h.p. Sunbeam Gurkha

250 h.p. Sunbeam Maori (later designated Maori I)

260 h.p. Sunbeam Maori II (double ignition)

275 h.p. Sunbeam Maori III (improved)

⬆ *9041 with wings folded*

⬆ *N1274 Short 184 Improved type being launched at Calshot*

⬆ *W/T installation (Robt. W. Paul type 52 No.138). Generator is hinged in the stowed position*

⬆ *Short 184 production Coultham Street works*

⬆ *N2900 in the Great Northern Station yard, Lincoln*

The seaplane was also powered by a 240 h.p. Renault engine known as the 'Renault Mercedes' because of its aluminium castings.

Early Robey Short 184s had one .303 inch Lewis machine gun on a Whitehouse mounting in the rear cockpit. Most machines had a Scarff No. 2 gun ring mounting for the Lewis gun as standard. The warload was widely varied from a $14\frac{1}{2}$ inch torpedo slung between the floats or a bomb load of up to 520lb slung on racks beneath the fuselage. Numbers 9045-9050 were completed as Type D single-seaters to carry nine 65lb bombs stowed in the space occupied by the front cockpit and suspended by their noses.

⬆ *Cockpit of N1260 (JMB/GSL)*

Late in 1917, one Robey machine, N2900, was displayed in the Great Northern Station yard to raise money for the Red Cross. In 1919 Robey's final Short 184 order was cancelled. It is not certain whether N9305 was completed. However, the firm certainly built a large scale model of this machine the fate of which is unknown. Of the last batch of Robey aircraft, four machines, N9290-3 were despatched to fight in North Russia in 1919.

⬆ *First Longhorn N5000 at Bracebridge Heath*

THE MAURICE FARMAN LONGHORN

In May, 1916, Robeys received an order for thirty Maurice Farman School aircraft of the 'Longhorn' pusher type. These machines were tested at the Bracebridge Heath aerodrome where Robey's had a wooden aircraft shed beside the hospital cemetery wall.

Only sixteen of the Robey Farmans were built as the order was partly cancelled. Most of these were used as trainers at Killingholme and Eastbourne. Records survive showing the history of the first ten machines as follows:

N5000 *Continuously used at Eastbourne, condemned March 1918*
N5001
N5002 *Broken up for spares by January 1918*
N5003
N5004 *Wrecked at Killingholme*
N5005 *Cannibalised by January 1918*
N5006 *Wrecked at Eastbourne late 1917*
N5007 *Cannibalised by January 1918*
N5008 *Wrecked at Eastbourne*
N5009 *Scrapped 21.4.1918 - frame and fabric deteriorated*
N5010-16 *Transferred to the R.F.C.*

The Robey Farmans were powered by the 75 h.p. Rolls Royce Hawk engine.

⬆ *N5000*

4260

The second machine in the works

No.1 M/c READY FOR TEST
1st. TEST GAVE PERFECT PERFORMANCE.
PILOT. CAPT. HAMMOND. HE WAS DELIGHTED WITH IT.

Robey Peters 9498 - contemporary caption

THE ROBEY PETERS FIGHTING MACHINE

Few test flights can end more precariously than
atop an asylum but that was the fate of the
extraordinary aeroplane designed by J.A. Peters.
Fitted with a large Rolls Royce engine the Robey
Peters was a three seater in which the pilot was
positioned at the rear of the fuselage, flanked by
two gunners in the wing.

In front of the Robey's Aerodrome shed. Clayton built Sopwith Triplanes inside

Equipped with a 300 round Lewis gun (port nacelle) and a ten round Davis gun (starboard), the Peters was the most impressive of the early gun machines. The Davis, a heavy recoilless gun of American origin, was then highly regarded by the Admiralty who proposed to fit it to their scouts and seaplanes for coastal Zeppelin and U-boat patrols. A huge affair, the two pounder version fitted being just over seven feet long, the gun was loaded at the centre of its double length barrels. The recoil was eliminated by the emission of a contra charge fired down the rearward facing barrel as the shell was fired.

Eight of the shells, about twenty inches in length, were stored in racks along the sides of the front bay of the starboard nacelle. The remaining two were slotted into the wing, outboard of the rear (gunner's) bay. Enclosed in their metal nosed plywood nacelles, the two observer/gunners were amply protected from the rigours of aerial warfare by the wing structure, and, in the event of a ground loop, by the guns which were mounted on rails above the nacelle.

No.2 machine

Peters in the gun nacelle

↑ *Paintshop, Robey Peters No.1 wings and Short 184 parts may be seen*

Design work commenced in February 1916. Construction of the first machine, 9498, started on the 17th April, and the engine was received at the Works early in June. Although it had been hoped that it would be ready for flying by mid-June, 9498 was not completed until September when it was taken to 'Robey's Aerodrome' at Bracebridge Heath near Lincoln for testing. A Davis gun had been installed for the tests but ballast replaced the ammunition for the flight trials.

↑↓ *The crash (contemporary caption)*

🔼 *Wing covering shop*

The first test flight was completely successful when a circuit of the airfield was made. However, the machine was slightly damaged on the second flight trial when it overturned. Three days later on return from a flight to Cranwell, the machine plunged onto the roof of the mental hospital adjoining the airfield. Due to a breakdown in engine control, the machine caught fire at low altitude. The wing was damaged by this fire and a metal part of the machine fell in the garden of the village school whilst the big biplane itself crashed on the hospital, piercing the roof. Damage to the extent of £50 was caused to the building by the ensuing fire. Although the machine was almost completely destroyed, the pilot, New Zealander Capt. Joseph Hammond, was unhurt and subsequently tested the second machine.

The Robey Peters II (9499) was completed under mysterious circumstances with many design improvements, notably a new equal span wing and a fin was added in the hope of improving the design of the earlier machine. This second aircraft was cancelled by the Admiralty, this cancellation (undated) being noted in Robey's order book. Nevertheless, it left the Lincoln works in spring 1917 for Robey's shed at Bracebridge Heath, beside the hospital cemetery. The official serial, 9499, was not borne by the machine, but the constructor's No. 76 was

applied to the port fuselage side below the tailplane shortly before flight testing.

No. 76, which was to have carried two Davis guns certainly looked very promising. It was also fitted with two side windows to improve landing visibility. Air brakes, at the rear of top and bottom wing centre sections, were retained and a later variant of what was to become the Rolls Royce 'Eagle' engine was fitted.

The first flight which had been delayed by bad weather took place on Easter Sunday 8th April 1917. However, success again eluded the venture. Much to the dismay of the local villagers who had gathered for the occasion, the aircraft stalled on take off and crashed near the perimeter of the airfield. It is likely that Hammond, a pilot of exceptional skill, applied aileron correction only to find that the aileron controls were crossed. Miraculously, Capt. J. J. Hammond escaped again having earlier quit freelancing for testing less hazardous mounts in the products of the British and Colonial Aeroplane Company. Peters also left after the demise of his fated brainchild to join the Alliance Aeroplane Company. Post war he designed the Seabird of somewhat similar size and appearance which he was to have piloted in the Atlantic Flight Competition.

THE ROBEY SEAPLANE

In February 1917 J. A. Peters started design work on a single seat seaplane to carry two 65lb bombs stowed vertically inside the fuselage. The design showed influences of the Short 184 and the Robey Peters and was to have been powered by a 200 h.p. Hispano Suiza V-8 (Adder) engine. A contract for one machine was placed on 16th April 1917 and on 7th May following, the contract was increased to three machines. However, the type, HBS2 as it was known, was dropped when Peters left Lincoln in the summer.

MISCELLANY

Robeys continued to build Short 184 aircraft until after the Armistice. In 1918 Robey & Co. built ten tanks as a final contribution to the war effort.

Towards the end of World War 2, two prototype two-stroke aero-engines, designed by A. Castellini, were built and tested in the small engine test shop.

No details of these tests have been traced, nor the fate of the engines but their design output would appear rather optimistic! The Lindum engine, a sixteen cylinder two row radial, 154 mm bore and 176 mm stroke, total swept volume 52.45 litres, with two stage supercharging, was reputed to deliver 6500 h.p. and weigh only 1891 lb! The diameter was 55^3/$_4$" and length 54".

The second engine was a V-12, with the same cylinder measurements, swept volume 39.3 litres, output 3000 h.p. on petrol, weighing only 1204 lb. A projected diesel version 15:1 compression ratio, was to weigh 1330 lb. The novel feature of these engines was the feeder piston, fitted with two poppet valves, operated from the connecting rods. It would be interesting to know the results of the tests.

Other WW2 production included: depth charge cases and chutes, corvette engines, steam generating sets for degaussing minesweepers, and gun mountings including a 4.5" Vickers naval gun prototype which was never developed.

After the war, Robey's traditional business declined and they were eventually taken over. The Globe Works site in Canwick Road is currently occupied by Jackson Building Centres Ltd., one of the largest builders merchants in the East Midlands. Bays 8 and 9 which were the main aircraft shops are now 'Pelham House', the group's head office and showrooms.

CLAYTON & SHUTTLEWORTH
LIMITED

CLAYTON AND SHUTTLEWORTH LTD WAS FOUNDED IN 1842 WHEN NATHANIEL CLAYTON AND JOSEPH SHUTTLEWORTH SET UP AN IRON FOUNDRY BESIDE THE RIVER WITHAM. THEIR FIRST INTEREST WAS IN AGRICULTURAL MACHINERY. LATER STEAM ENGINES AND THRESHING MACHINES BECAME THE FIRM'S MAIN PRODUCTS. THE RIVERSIDE FACTORY EXPANDED WITH THE BUILDING OF THE 'TITANIC WORKS' SO NAMED AS BEING BUILT AT THE SAME TIME AND THE SAME LENGTH AS THE ATLANTIC LINER. THIS EXTENSION WAS SITUATED BETWEEN THE GREAT NORTHERN AND THE GREAT CENTRAL RAILWAY LINES, WHILST THE OLDER AND LARGER STAMP END WORKS WAS AT THE OTHER SIDE OF THE GREAT CENTRAL LINE. AT THE OUTBREAK OF THE GREAT WAR THE FIRM WAS ALSO MAKING RAILWAY ROLLING STOCK AND PIONEERING THE USE OF TRACKED VEHICLES. THEIR WORKS OCCUPIED ABOUT ONE HUNDRED ACRES AND THE FIRM HAD A PAYROLL OF ABOUT FIVE THOUSAND.

⬆ *Sea Scouts S.S.24 and S.S.25 at Pembroke 1.5.1917 with BE2c fuselages (JMB/GSL)*

THE S.S. AIRSHIP

Clayton and Shuttleworth's entry into the field of aviation was made early in 1916 with the manufacture of parts for S.S. (Sea Scout) airships operated by the Admiralty on coastal patrols. Claytons built tail stabilising planes for some of these machines and were also concerned with fuselage gondola work at the Stamp End works. The airships had horizontal stabilising planes with one ventral plane forming the controls. The machines were equipped with Royal Aircraft Factory B.E.2c fuselages, minus tail surfaces, as crew gondolas. The firm would appear to have rebuilt at least one B.E.2c fuselage fitted with a 75 h.p. Renault engine, including a nine foot diameter four blade propeller as made for such a machine.

These non-rigid 'blimps' proved most useful in submarine hunting and nearly one hundred were built during the war by various contractors.

THE SOPWITH TRIPLANE

The first type of aeroplane to be built by Claytons was the Sopwith Triplane. At Kingston-upon-Thames, Herbert Smith designed the machine early in 1916 to replace the Sopwith Pup. The Sopwith prototype showed such a phenomenal rate of climb and excellent manoeuvrability that the test pilot, Harry Hawker, looped the machine on its first flight.

Both the War Office and the Admiralty ordered the machine, Claytons receiving contracts from both departments. Serial numbers A9813-9978 were allocated for 166 Royal Flying Corps aircraft and forty, N5350 - 5389, for the Royal Naval Air Service. Due to political pressures, however, only the Admiralty received Triplanes, deliveries commencing late in 1916. A Sopwith built machine N5420, was sent to Lincoln as a pattern aircraft and the first Clayton built Triplane was delivered on the 2nd December, 1916. Production aircraft were fitted with the 130 h.p. Clerget 9B rotary engine.

↑ *N5350 the first Clayton built Sopwith Triplane at Bracebridge Heath late in 1916. Philip Warwick Robson Clayton & Shuttleworth's managing director is talking to the pilot (JMB/GSL)*

↑ *N5350 (JMB/GSL)* ↓

↻ Captured Clayton Triplane (JMB/GSL)

The Clayton machines were built in the eastern half of the Titanic works and, after assembly, were pushed outside for engine running tests. After this, the aircraft were dismantled and taken to Robey's aerodrome at Bracebridge Heath for test flying followed by delivery flights. This procedure was later followed with Sopwith Camel aircraft, the machines often being flown direct to France. An additional batch of Triplanes was built after the first order, N533-8 being fitted with twin Vickers guns and N541-3 going to the French Government. Production of the Triplane then gave way to the legendary Sopwith Camel, the Triplane not having sufficient power to carry two guns successfully under combat conditions. A report suggests that the last Clayton-built Triplane crashed in a corner of the hospital cemetery adjoining Robey's aerodrome.

↻ Triplane N5364 at Farnborough 15.5.1917

↻ N5357 in front of Robey's Aerodrome shed. Robey Farman inside the shed (JMB/GSL)

↻ Another view of N5357

THE SOPWITH F1 CAMEL

Clayton and Shuttleworth became the fourth contractor to build the Sopwith Camel, receiving an order in March 1917. The type remained in production at the Titanic works until 1919. Delivery of the first batch was made at the turn of the year. These were fitted with Clerget engines and were delivered mainly to the Royal Naval Air Service. Several of the machines (detailed in the appendix) went to the Belgian government, one machine still being in existence. Some aircraft from the second batch went to the Greeks.

After delivery of the first batch, most Clayton Camels for the R.N.A.S. were powered by the 150 h.p. Bentley designed BR1 rotary engine. Such Camels equipped 209 Squadron of the Royal Air Force when Captain Roy Brown was officially credited with shooting down Manfred von Richthofen on 21st April 1918, flying B7270. The other British aircraft involved in the Incident piloted by Captain E. R. May, was being followed by Richthofen when the latter was killed by gun fire. The official credit went to the newly formed Royal Air Force but the matter is still subject to controversy. Claytons Issued a souvenir leaflet on the incident after the war. The firm built seven batches of FI Camels.

⬆ B7270 Camel and Captain Roy Brown (Chaz Bowyer)

⬆ Scout aircraft production at Titanic Works. The building is now called Witham Park. Sopwith Camels can be seen being built in the picture

⬆ B5690 Camel crash (JMB/GSL)

⬆ Clayton steam wagon with a delivery of Sopwith Camel wings to the West Common (Museum of Lincolnshire Life)

⊕ *B7230 3 Sqn RNAS after capture (JMB/GSL)*

⊕ *B7230 forced down on 18th March 1918 (JMB/GSL)*

⊕ *B7234 213 Sqn (JMB/GSL)*

⊕ Camel B5743 (JMB/GSL)

⊕ B7268 Camel (JMB/GSL)

⊕ D9638 203 Sqn R.A.F. force landed at Noyelles sur l'Escaut, France 8th October 1918

SOPWITH 2F1 CAMEL

In 1917, a version of the Camel appeared for use on ships, with the B.R.1 engine standardised for the type. The main variations were a reduction in wingspan, the rear fuselage being detachable for stowage, and a difference in armament which retained a single Vickers gun fitted on the left with a Lewis gun mounted above the wing.

Claytons received an order for fifty such machines but full delivery cannot be confirmed. The company did not move on to build the Camel's successor, the Snipe as production was concentrated on large bomber aircraft at the end of the war.

↥ B7275 Camel (JMB/GSL)

↥ D3372 Camel crash (JMB/GSL)

↥ Line up of Sopwith 2F1 Camels N8204 shown nearest to camera (JMB/GSL)

HANDLEY PAGE 0/400 BOMBER

A National Aircraft Factory was originally planned for Lincoln, to be managed by Clayton and Shuttleworth to meet the growing demand for larger aircraft for the proposed Independent Air Force. The plans were changed, and in late 1916 work started on the third Clayton and Shuttleworth works, which was bounded by the River Witham to the south and the Great Central railway line to the north. A prisoner of war camp was built to the west of the plant and the prisoners were put to work building aircraft shops at the large Abbey and Tower works.

Contract No. A.S.28197, for fifty Handley Page 0/400 machines with Rolls Royce Eagle VIII engines, was given to the company on October 4th 1917 with works order number 11/3333. The most southerly part of the Abbey works, recognised by its saw-tooth shaped roof, was the erecting shop where the machines were assembled three abreast. The bombers were towed out of the shop to the field east of the works alongside the river. As they were over twenty feet high, the machines had to be flown out for testing and delivery. The field (now subdivided) is still known as Handley Page Field. The aircraft were lightly loaded for the short ferry flight to the Aircraft Acceptance Park.

⬆ *Clayton & Shuttleworth workers posed with a Handley Page in the Abbey works erecting shop*

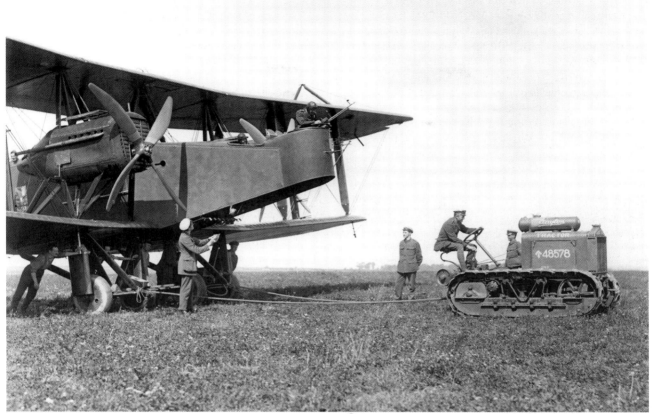

🠕 *Clayton crawler tractor with a Handley Page 29.8.1918*

🠕 *D9703 Handley Page with wings folded (JMB/GSL)*

🠕 *D9702 Handley Page 0/400 (Chaz Bowyer)*

VICKERS VIMY

The Company received contract 35A/1030/C835 for one hundred Vickers Vimy bombers fitted with either B.H.P. or Fiat A12 bis engines in May 1918, followed by a further order for fifty machines, contract 35A/2978/C3411. Both orders were cancelled soon after the Armistice and only three machines were completed at the Abbey works.

Mr. A. E. Codling, then a clerk at the factory, recalls the scene: *"One of the Vickers type machines was flown off the Clayton airfield. I remember the machine very well as the engines for it came from overseas - I think they were Italian and they had been in store for so long that they could not get them to start. A group of some twenty airmen were brought in and, for three whole days, they formed a series of chains to pull the propellers round to get the engines to fire. At last the engines started up and they were run for several hours to get them loosened up. The machine was then towed out to the flying field ground and they had further trouble with the engines which was overcome by carrying hot water to the aeroplane.*

"The machine took off and did, as near as I can say, a forty-five minute flight around Lincoln and area. Another machine was half complete when work stopped".

Mr. Codling adds that the erection shop foreman was Mr. Riley, wing assembly foreman Mr. Coulson and the works manager was Mr. Woods. Mr. Panther was the works manager at the Titanic works.

CLAYTON AND SHUTTLEWORTH MISCELLANY

On 9th April, 1918, King George V & Queen Mary visited Lincoln touring the works of Ruston Proctor & Co. Ltd., Wm. Foster Ltd., Clayton & Shuttleworth Ltd. and in the afternoon, Robey & Co. Ltd and the military hospital. The Royal party was conducted round the Titanic works by the Managing Director, Mr. Robson, and treated to a display of aerobatics by a newly built Clayton Camel over the works.

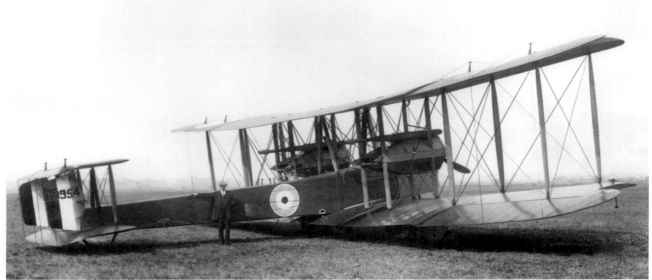

⊕ *Vickers built Fiat A12 powered Vimy prototype (Vickers)*

↑ *B7280 fuselage on display Krakow, Poland (Jan Hoffman)*

One Clayton and Shuttleworth aircraft left is the Sopwith Camel serial SC11 (ex B5747) exhibited in the Musee de l'Armee et d'Histoire Militaire in Brussels. The fuselage of Bentley powered Camel B7280 (210 Sqn. R.A.F.) is on display at the Muzeum Lotnictwa, Krakow, Poland. The airframe had logged 155 hours and the engine 15 when it was reported missing after a patrol on September the 15th 1918. It is believed that the machine was flown by the Germans before exhibition in the Berlin Air Museum post war. The exhibits were evacuated to Poland during World War II; only the fuselage arrived in Krakow.

↑ *Clayton Tractor with a DH4 (P H T Green)*

In the western half of the Titanic works, Clayton & Shuttleworth built crawler tractors for the War Department from 1917 to 1919. These were used, amongst other things, for towing large aircraft. They were fitted with either 35 or 40 h.p. Dorman Stafford 4 cylinder side valve engines, some petrol driven, others diesel. The tractors cost around £600 each in 1919. An example is displayed at the Museum of Lincolnshire Life.

Penney and Porter Ltd., whose works was then situated in Broadgate (now the site of the telephone exchange), took on sub-contract work from Claytons. They made fuel tanks for Sopwiths and fabricated engine cowls, also making bullet proof steel fuel tanks for the Handley Pages.

⊕ *Mast head gear for Cardington*

⊙ *Mast head for Karachi*

After a series of changes on the board, Sir William McClintock was appointed Receiver and Manager in June 1929 and Liquidator in February 1930. The Company was finally wound up in December 1936. The patent rights of the firm were sold off, principally to Marshalls of Gainsborough, and Babcock & Wilcox, who used Stamp End boiler works from 1924 to 1932. The Forge became the Smith Clayton Forge and Clayton Dewandre Co. Ltd. took over the Titanic works in 1928.

In 1924, the Labour Government launched their Empire communications scheme for an airship service to India and Canada, the former route, from Cardington in Bedfordshire, via Ismailia (Egypt) and Karachi (India) was expected to be extended, eventually, to Australia. Airship mooring masts were an essential part of the scheme and Babcock & Wilcox Ltd., whilst in Lincoln, designed and built mast head mooring gears for Cardington, Ismailia, Montreal and Karachi. They were an unusual job, being the first of their kind, and the contract was won in open competition and ordered by the Air Ministry.

Their purpose was to provide a simple and relatively cheap means of docking an airship with ready access for passengers, loading and unloading of cargo, and for refueling. Two airships were ordered, one to be built by the Government at Cardington, and one by the Airship Guarantee Corporation, a subsidiary of Vickers, at Howden in Yorkshire, a disused R.N.A.S. station.

A Clayton and Shuttleworth Handley Page four blade propeller is on display at the Shuttleworth Aeroplane Collection Museum at Old Warden, Biggleswade, Bedfordshire. The Company also made propellers for other firms, making some two blade propellers for Sunbeam engines for Robeys, also four blade propellers for the Galloway engine.

The Clayton and Shuttleworth Company was a victim of the post war slump. The Chairman of the firm, millionaire industrialist Alfred Shuttleworth resigned on 22nd February, 1919 and died in 1925 leaving his estate to his nephew Richard Shuttleworth who founded the Shuttleworth Aeroplane Collection before he was killed whilst an R.A.F. pilot in 1940.

The airships were expected to transport many tons of mail and general cargo and about one hundred passengers, weighing upwards of 150 tons in total. A working load of 15 tons was assumed on the gears, the completed mast being loaded to 30 tons under test.

The main feature of the gear, the gimbal system, worked on the same principle as the gimbal lamps used on ships, so contrived that they will swing in any direction as the ship rolls or pitches.

The system, weighing 28 tons, is like a pendulum or plumb-bob which can swing in any direction about the gimbal centre, and is well illustrated in the photos taken in the Stamp End works.

The gear consisted of a steel gimbal casting, containing a square riveted structure carrying motors and gearing operating an inner rack with squared tube about 19' 4" long, sliding in bronze guides. Within this square tube was a circular tube counter-weighted to move outwards with an upward load of one ton. A second motor with gearing operated four rope drums used for centring the whole apparatus under load. To receive an airship, a rope was passed from the top of the cone down the mast to the main hauling winch carrying 3,000 feet of rope allowing ample slack to allow the airship to ride as it approached its moorings, its nose cone finally being hauled into the cup at the top of the mast head.

The Mast Head Gear, erected at Cardington in 1926 by Babcock & Wilcox, proved perfectly satisfactory under test, no important changes being found necessary despite the experimental nature of the installation. The whole of the boiler installation, oil firing gear and winches were also installed by the company.

The first airship to use the mast was the R.33 which was moored under Major G. H. Scott's direction in a demonstration organised for the Dominion Premiers present for the Imperial Conference in 1926. The Ismailia gear was erected later in 1929 followed by that at Karachi.

The Cardington mast, 202ft high and 70ft diameter at the base of the legs was the first ever cantilever mooring mast to be built. It was dismantled for scrap in 1943.

⬆ *Mast head gear for Karachi seen in Stamp End works*

↑ Airship R33 moored to the mast at Cardington, note the two Gloster Grebe biplanes stowed under the airship. November 1926

A. V. ROE & COMPANY
LIMITED

AVRO AIRCRAFT REPAIR

In the run up to the Second World War a significant expansion of the British aircraft industry began. The resurgence of German militarism led the Government to commence a major re-equipment programme for the RAF and it would have been logical to assume that, just as in the previous war, Lincoln with its major engineering facilities would be well placed to handle large contracts for aircraft and engines. For a number of reasons this did not take place. Aircraft production was concentrated in areas of the midlands and the west with access to large pools of labour experienced in mass production and further away from the threat of air attack from the East Coast. 'Shadow' aircraft factories were built and contracted out to large motor manufacturers such as the Rootes Group and the Nuffield Organisation to manage. There was, however, the need for major repair facilities to support operational RAF airfields and in 1940 the Repair Organisation was born. This was set up to establish a link between the units of a rapidly expanding Bomber Command and the Avro factories which were just beginning to supply Manchester bombers to RAF squadrons based in Lincolnshire.

It became apparent that a central headquarters would have to be established to co-ordinate the volume of repair work which arose. In May 1941 the Ministry of Supply requisitioned all of the buildings on the Bracebridge Heath site for aircraft repair and salvage work with the exception of the centre bay of three hangars used by the Lincolnshire Road Car Co. As the war effort intensified, the Manchester was replaced by the Lancaster and as it came into service in large numbers the Repair Organisation expanded rapidly. At a time when Bomber Command was pressing for as many aircraft as possible to take part in 'Ops', Avro personnel worked side by side with the RAF ground crews until the very last minute before take off in order to ensure a maximum effort by the Squadrons.

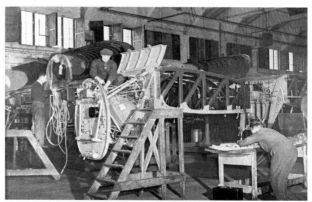

⬆ *Work on Lancaster centre sections in the WWI single hangar*

⬆ *Women workers cutting damage off Lancaster L7544 (Hulton-Getty)*

Mr. C L Hatton and Mr. F C Langton were mainly responsible for the building up of the new organisation; a mammoth task when it is considered that proper equipment was not readily available and the majority of labour was new to the industry. New labour was not the only problem however, major problems were created by the need for special repair schemes to enable flak damaged aircraft to be put back into service. Bomb doors appeared particularly susceptible and one Avro worker recalls large quantities of damaged doors stored at the rear of the site awaiting repair.

A repair Design Office was created and with the able assistance of Mr. G Whitehead many problems were solved and aircraft otherwise destined for the scrapheap were put back into useful service. The works were extended and a B1 hangar was erected along with additional workshops, offices, stores and canteen facilities. Aircraft that were slightly damaged were repaired and transported, with the outer wing sections removed, via the A15 to nearby RAF Waddington where Hangar No.5 (at the Harmston end) was taken over for re-assembly and test flying.

Avro had also foreseen the need for a new factory and facilities at RAF Langar near Nottingham were opened in 1942 to cope with the assembly of Lancaster and Manchester aircraft. These aircraft were put together from an assortment of components which were resurrected from squadron graveyards up and down the country and repaired by an army of sub-contractors. It says much for the excellent degree of inter-changeability that no major difficulties in assembly were experienced. When a damaged aircraft was received at Bracebridge Heath the log book was forwarded to Langar and assigned to the rebuild; however in many cases very little if any of the original aircraft was part of the new one. Fuselage sections were repaired on site while the wings went to the L.M.S. railway workshops at Derby. Queen Mary low loaders were a common sight in Lincoln streets, en route to Bracebridge or Waddington with sections of bombers.

Early in 1942 the White Hart Garage in Lincoln was also requisitioned. This unit was employed solely in salvage and reconditioning bolts, nuts and washers and similar small parts from crashed aircraft and they also sorted out small items such as rivets and screws swept up from factory floors. The work was carried out exclusively by part time female labour.

Avro also set up a Repair Co-ordinating Stores Depot on behalf of the Ministry of Aircraft Production which was responsible for supplying all of the Repair Group factories. If an aircraft was grounded awaiting spares then a telegram starting

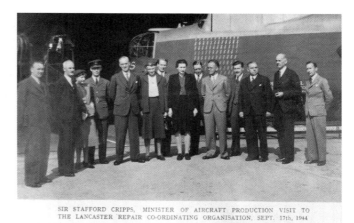

SIR STAFFORD CRIPPS, MINISTER OF AIRCRAFT PRODUCTION VISIT TO THE LANCASTER REPAIR CO-ORDINATING ORGANISATION, SEPT. 17th, 1944

⊕ *Sir Stafford Cripps and his party in front of Lancaster R5868*

with AOG (Aircraft on Ground) would be sent in for an immediate despatch of the part required.

The rapid expansion of the Repair Group factories was accompanied by the equally rapid expansion of outworking repair parties organised by Mr. F C Langton. A tremendous volume of work passed through the hands of the outworking staff that at its peak numbered well over five hundred. For a long period, parties were putting over thirty aircraft per week back into operational service. Modification work was also carried out, and many special aircraft were prepared for missions such as the raids on the Mohne and Eder dams and Augsburg. At its peak in 1943 Bracebridge Heath employed 1,582 people including shift-workers and outworkers and by the end of the War the Repair Organisation had returned over 4,000 aircraft to the RAF that would otherwise have been lost.

In 1944 the Empire Central Navigation School at RAF Shawbury was made responsible for improving long range navigation techniques to prepare for training aircrew for the war in the Pacific. On 6th September 1944 Lancaster B1 PD328 was delivered to the Avro Repair Unit at RAF Waddington where the dorsal turret was removed and replaced with a second astrodome. Over the next six months this aircraft embarked upon a series of long-range flights and on completion returned for further work. This included the installation of extra fuel tanks, replacing the remaining turrets with streamlined fairings and stripping the camouflage paint.

⊕ *Mrs Bird and Mrs West spraying Lancaster rear fuselage*

This was completed at Waddington in 9 days by working round the clock and on its return to Shawbury it was named 'Aries'. A series of flights over the Arctic were conducted to confirm the position of the North Geographic and Magnetic Poles and further long range flights took place after the war ended. Aries was retired in January 1947 but ECNS continued the long-range work and it was successively replaced by two Lincolns, Aries II and Aries III which were modified to a similar standard at Langar.

At the end of World War II the Avro Repair factories were busily engaged on repair and modifications of Avro Lincoln bombers and York transports. Included among these was Avro York MW107 which was converted over a period of 10 days into a V.I.P. transport for Field Marshal Smuts. Part of the work involved wood panelling the interior to a very high standard and the camouflage paint was stripped off and replaced with a highly polished metal finish. On completion it was transferred to the South African Air Force as serial no. 4999 and named 'Oubaas'. The factory overhauled the majority of the Avro Anson trainers and communications aircraft retained by the Royal Air Force for peacetime use. Bracebridge Heath also completed design work and conversion of 'Classroom Training' Ansons for the Royal Navy and repaired and returned innumerable components of all types to RAF Maintenance Units.

Lancaster bombers were converted into Lancastrian transports by removing military equipment that was no longer required; this included the gun turrets, which were replaced by streamlined fairings at the nose and tail. Four of these were converted for British South American Airways (PP688, PP689, PP690 & PP751) however they were only used for about a year as they proved uneconomic in service. The RAF was desperately short of transports after the War as most of the Dakotas supplied under 'lend-lease' arrangements had been returned to the U.S.A. and the Yorks and Lancastrians were urgently pressed into service for the Berlin Airlift in 1948-49.

Lancasters and Lincolns were modified to suit the individual needs of customers in the Argentine, Egypt and France and a special flying training school was established at Langar to train Argentinean crews for duties with the aircraft that had been prepared for them.

Views of the instrument repair shop

Other Lancasters and Lincolns were specially prepared as flying test beds for jet engine development work in Britain and Sweden.

Throughout the time that the Repair Organisation was based in Lincoln it had no serious flying mishaps, in spite of the fact that for quite some time it was without an accredited test pilot. In the early stages service personnel did the test flying and later on Squadron Leader Field-Richards was allocated as a Ministry of Aircraft Production test pilot and he continued with Avro after his demobilisation.

⬆ MW107 Smut's York at Waddington May 1945

⬆ Smut's York seen later as 4999 Oubaas in South Africa (SAAF)

⬆ Lincoln RE312 at Waddington 29th May 1946 for a civic flight. Left to right: C.L.Hatton, works manager, Miss Lou Neave, trainee flight engineer, Sqn.Ldr. F.J. Fields-Richards, Avro test pilot, F.C. Langton, assistant works manager, Lincolnshire Echo Gossiper Fred Morton, Mayor Ald. J.W.F. (later Sir Francis) Hill, and town clerk Mr J. Harper-Smith (Lincolnshire Echo)

⬆ *G-AGUK Star Gold BSAAC Lancastrian at Waddington*

⬆ *Avro workers in front of converted Lancastrian G-AGUL Star Watch (PP 690) April 1946. Crashed Heathrow 23.10.1947*

⬆ *Lincoln Aries II RE364*

❶ Dambuster film Lancaster at R.A.F. Hemswell

❶ A.V. Roe Queen Mary aircraft transporter carrying workers into Lincoln during a bus strike, seen at Newark Road Cross O Cliff Hill junction (Lincolnshire Echo)

❶ Anson G-AGPG used by Avro as executive transport, regularly overhauled at Bracebridge Heath (R.C.B. Ashworth)

🔼 Anson being towed up the A15 to Waddington, note the tilting road signs (Lincolnshire Echo)

Shortly after the War the Air Staff issued Specification B35/46 for a high altitude jet bomber with the capability to deliver a nuclear weapon. This was the origin of Britain's V-Bombers, the Vickers Valiant, the Handley Page Victor, and the Avro Vulcan. The Avro design team's proposal represented a huge leap forward in terms of speed, altitude and range over contemporary aircraft and the choice of the untried delta wing configuration presented many risks. In order to evaluate potential problems two small-scale prototypes were proposed; the one-third scale Avro 707 for low speed research and the half scale Avro 710 to investigate high mach numbers at altitude. The Avro 710 was discontinued because of the large amount of development it required which would have distracted attention from the full scale prototypes. However, as the 707s could be built relatively quickly using components from other aircraft, the programme went ahead and Specification E15/48 was issued to cover these. Five Avro 707s were built, the first three were completed at Woodford and two further machines, the single seat Avro 707A WZ736 and the two seat Avro 707C WZ744, were completed at Bracebridge Heath. These were assembled from components fabricated in Manchester and first flew from RAF Waddington on February 20th and 1st July 1953 respectively, giving them the distinction of being the last two aircraft built in Lincoln.

The development of the full-scale aircraft overtook the Avro 707 programme and by the time they flew it was too late for them to provide any significant data for the Vulcan's development apart from in one critical area. When the Vulcan prototype was flying at high speed at altitude, application of 'G' could initiate buffeting at the wing leading edge. Wing fences were tried but they failed to cure the problem and the eventual solution was to change the straight leading edge to one with compound sweep. When the third Avro 707, WD280, was damaged in a landing accident it was sent to Bracebridge Heath for repair. The opportunity was taken to modify the wing shape which allowed the new profile to be tried quickly before embarking on a major redesign of the full scale aircraft.

All three of the Avro 707s worked on at Bracebridge Heath were subsequently used on various research projects not connected with the Vulcan programme and on retirement they were all preserved. At the time of writing the single seat 707A WZ736 is on display in the Manchester Museum of Science and Industry and the two seat 707C WZ744 is at RAF Cosford. WD280 was shipped to Australia in 1956 for boundary layer tests and it subsequently went to the RAAF Museum at Point Cook.

Shortly after the Avro 707C was completed, the Bracebridge Heath workers were given a job which was a complete contrast. An Avro 504K trainer, D7560, had been allocated to the Science Museum after the First World War and in 1934 it was moved to Hull.

🔼 Anson repair line B1 hangar

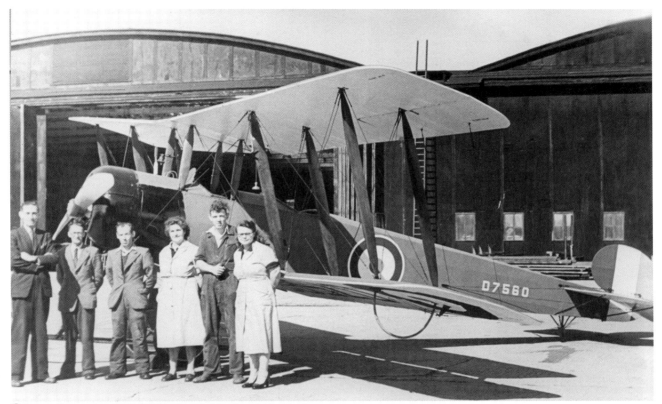

⊙ *Science Museum Avro 504K D7560 after rebuild at Bracebridge Heath*

By 1953 it was in poor condition having been stored outside during the Second World War and it was sent to Bracebridge Heath for restoration. The biplane, which was powered by a Ruston built Clerget engine, was restored to exhibition condition and returned to the main Museum in London. At the time of writing it was on display at the Museum of Army Flying, Middle Wallop.

Several other biplanes were also restored by Bracebridge Heath workers as they were one of the few units of the Hawker Siddeley Group that could still handle fabric work. These included the Avro Tutor, Hawker Tomtit, Hawker Hart and a de Havilland Rapide belonging to the Group. The Tutor and the Tomtit were later acquired by the Shuttleworth Collection and the Hart went on display in the RAF Museum.

Another unusual assignment for the Repair organisation was the conversion of three Lancaster BVIIs for the film 'The Dambusters'. The aircraft, NX673, NX679 & NX782, had to be modified to simulate the BI (Special) Lancasters which carried the bouncing bomb. The weapon was still on the 'Secret List' in 1953 so the end product was what the film makers thought it would have looked like rather than an accurate reproduction of Barnes Wallis' invention. The bomb doors were removed and the ends of the bomb bays were faired in. Large 'bouncing bombs' were fabricated from plywood and plaster of Paris. The aircraft were based at RAF Hemswell for most of the filming with location work at Scampton and Kirton in Lindsey.

⊕ *Avro 707A WZ736 leaving the gates at Bracebridge Heath*

Bracebridge Heath was also used as a production facility for a number of Hawker Siddeley Group products including parts for Lancaster and Lincoln bombers, Shackleton maritime patrol aircraft, Meteor fighters, Avro 748 airliners, Armstrong Whitworth Argosy transports and Vulcan bombers. Avro representatives served the Repair Group interests all over the world, including Italy, India, Australia, Argentina, Egypt, Canada and Gibraltar. It also continued to be the base for teams of outworkers that carried out repairs and modifications to service aircraft at RAF airfields and housed the technical publications team that supported the Nimrod force in later years.

⊕ *On the snowbound A15 (Lincolnshire Echo)*

⬆ 707C WZ744 (N. Franklin)

⬆ Leaving the A15 to enter R.A.F. Waddington (Lincolnshire Echo)

⬆ Farnborough September 1953 display flypast of Vulcan prototypes VX777 (front), VX770 (rear) and the four Avro 707s (top), WZ736, VX790, WZ744, WD280 (bottom) (Avro photo by Paul Cullerne)

One interesting job that the outworkers were called to deal with was the repair of two aircraft that were damaged in landing accidents on the same day. On 15th August 1967 an Avro 748 airliner, G-ATEK of Channel Airways Ltd., slid off the runway at Portsmouth Airport and struck an embankment. Two hours later, its sister aircraft G-ATEH also over-ran and broke through the perimeter fence onto a main road. Fortunately, no one was injured in either of these incidents which were caused by the inability of the 748s to stop safely on a very wet grass airfield. Two teams were despatched to Portsmouth to repair the airliners on site; this entailed some major engineering work as the undercarriage, flaps and under-

⊕ *Avro 748 being transported across Portsmouth airfield, note damage by towing cable aft of door (John Ainsworth)*

⊕ *Repairs under a makeshift shelter, Portsmouth (John Ainsworth)*

surfaces of both aircraft had suffered severe damage in the accidents and subsequent recovery. Design authority from Avro was needed to sanction the rebuild of the fuselage main frames as otherwise these would have had to be rebuilt from scratch in production jigs.

Duncan Sandys' 1957 Defence White Paper led to a substantial reduction in the number of aircraft operated by the British armed forces and by the end of the decade almost all of the Ansons, Lincolns and Meteors had been retired which reduced the workload of the Repair Organisation. Avro retained the more modern buildings vacating the World War 1 group of hangars in 1959. These were then taken over by E.H. Lee, a haulage contractor. In the late 1960s the Nimrod began to replace the Shackleton in the RAF maritime reconnaissance role and, as Langar was too small to handle this aircraft, it closed in September 1968 and the work was transferred to Bitteswell. A V Roe & Co Ltd. were formally incorporated into Hawker Siddeley Aviation in 1974 and this subsequently became the Manchester Division of British Aerospace plc.

In later years Vulcan support provided a substantial part of the workload at Bracebridge Heath. The last squadrons were phased out in the early part of the 1980s and British Aerospace announced that the site would close in March 1982.

This run down was briefly interrupted by a period of hectic activity during the Falklands conflict as a small number of Vulcans were modified for use in the South Atlantic and as tankers for in-flight refuelling. One squadron was retained until March 1984 to supplement the RAF's Victor tanker force and when it finally stood down British Aerospace were able to complete their closure plans.

Today, five of the original AAP Belfast truss hangars survive; one bay of three hangars is still used by haulage contractors E H Lee although they are in poor condition. The single hangar has been extensively refurbished for use as a car parts business and the centre bay is used as an industrial unit. Dalgety Agriculture Ltd. uses the MAP B1 hangar and adjoining buildings erected for A.V. Roe & Company. A number of other original features survive, including the WW2 gatehouse, armoury and the fence which has wide gates designed to allow large aircraft sections to be manoeuvred on to the A15.

↑ Aerial view of the Bracebridge Heath works in the 1950s

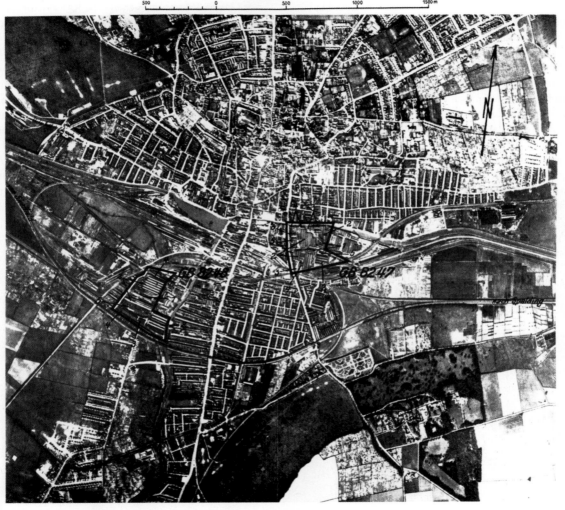

Lincoln

Dieselmotorenfabrik „Ruston and Hornsby Ltd."
Werk Ost (GB 8247), Werk West (GB 8248)

Länge (westl. Greenw.): 0° 32′ 18″   Breite: 53° 13′ 30″   Bildmitte
Mißweisung: — 10° 48′ (Mitte 1941)   Zielhöhe über NN 5 m

Maßstab etwa 1 : 15 800

Genst. 5. Abt. Oktober 1941

Karte 1 : 100 000
GB/E 14

⬆ *Luftwaffe target photo (1941) of Ruston's works*

RETROSPECTIVE

The industrial prosperity of the city peaked in the Great War. Much of the factory space built in those years is still in use today, and some of the machinery survived in use into the 1960s.

At the start of hostilities the aircraft industry consisted of a handful of pioneers with only a year or two of experience. The government looked to established engineers to develop aircraft production. The industrialists of the city were eager to respond, faced with little wartime demand for their traditional products and the loss of skilled workers to join the forces.

The supply of labour was to prove a major problem in both world wars. In WW1 younger male munitions workers were issued with 'on war work' certificates and badges to counter the white feather taunt. The introduction of conscription in 1916 exacerbated the problem and women workers took their place in munitions work. The part played by women on war work contributed to them being given the vote soon after the end of the Great War.

At the end of the war most of the engineering companies were in a strong position to diversify into new markets. Clayton & Shuttleworth were crippled by having built two very large works at the end of the war and the business was wound up in 1930. Smiths Stamping Works Ltd of Coventry bought the Forge (Tower Works) to form Smith Clayton Forge Ltd in 1929. Later, the adjacent Abbey Works was purchased. In 1936 the company received the first orders to supply Rolls Royce Ltd with components for Merlin & Kestrel engines.

During the Second World War Smith Clayton Forge made a variety of components for aero engines, including crankshafts for Armstrong Siddeley Cheetah, Rolls Royce Merlin and Vulture, Napier Sabre, Bristol Hercules and Centaurus engines. In addition, propeller hubs, airframe and undercarriage parts were made for Handley Page, Gloster, Lockheed, Austin & Dowty. Post War aircraft engine work continued. The company was taken over by Guest Keen & Nettlefold in 1963. Consideration was given to reopening Handley Page field as an airstrip for their executive light aircraft. Later GKN amalgamated with British Steel Special Steels division to form United Engineering Forgings.

In May 2000, UEF Aerospace became Wyman-Gordon (Lincoln) Ltd. The company continues to manufacture components for a wide range of civil and military engines, including Rolls Royce RB211, V2500, RTM322, Trent & Tay; BMW/RR BR710 and BR715, and the EJ200 for the Eurofighter Typhoon. Parts of the Handley Page erecting shop are now used as an AID bonded store for engine parts.

After the Second World War Rustons moved into gas turbine development. Dr G.B.R. Fielden, one of Sir Frank Whittle's pioneering Power Jets team headed the gas turbine design department. The company is now Alstom Power, a world leader in industrial gas turbines.

In recent years Sir William Tritton, the engineer behind Wm. Fosters' tank has been commemorated by a new road going through the WW1 tank testing ground. In a city proud of its engineering past there are surely many more names to remember. Up the hill at Bracebridge Heath the former hospital site is being developed as housing. The airfield buildings substantially survive in industrial use; the WW1 aircraft sheds are now Grade II listed buildings. On the West Common the foundations of the aircraft sheds behind Aldermans Walk may be traced and a 1917 R.F.C. crest adorns a fireplace in one of the rooms under the Grandstand.

⬆ *Aerial view of the Ruston aircraft factory taken in the 1950s. Many of the buildings are now used by Sinclair Horticulture & Leisure PLC for the production of garden supplies*

APPENDICES

AIRCRAFT BUILT BY RUSTON PROCTOR & CO. LTD. 1915-1919

(Ruston & Hornsby Ltd. after 11.9.1918)

SERIAL NOS	QUANTITY	TYPE	REMARKS
2670-2769	100	BE2c	90hp RAF 1a engine
6228-6258	31	BE2d	
6259-6327	69	BE2e	
7762-7811	50	Sopwith 1½ Strutter	110hp Clerget 9Z
A2381-2430	50	Sopwith 1½ Strutter	
A8141-8340	200	Sopwith 1½ Strutter	
B2301-2550	250	Sopwith Camel	130hp Clerget 9B
B2551-2600	50	Sopwith 1½ Strutter	
B5551-5650	100	Sopwith Camel	
B7281-7480	200	Sopwith Camel	
C8201-8300	100	Sopwith Camel	
D1776-1975	200	Sopwith Camel	
D8101-8250	150	Sopwith Camel	
E1401-1600	200	Sopwith Camel	
E7137-7336	200	Sopwith Camel	
E7337-7836	500	Sopwith Snipe	230hp BR2 engine. E7798 on from 8.1919 'to Oddfellows Hall, Thetford, to be finished off on our behalf by Portholme, Huntingdon'
F2008-2082	75	Sopwith Camel	
F3968-4067	100	Sopwith Camel	
H351-(650)	300	Sopwith Snipe	No engines fitted after H364 (10.9.1919). Remainder of batch incomplete. H450 not started (20.9.1919)

NOTES ON INDIVIDUAL RUSTON MACHINES

SERIAL NOS	TYPE	REMARKS
2071	BE2c	Built by Daimler, rebuilt by Rustons
2699	BE2c	Preserved IWM
2673	BE2c	Leefe-Robinson's aircraft 3.9.1916
2687	BE2c	'Tasmania' presentation machine
2757	BE2c	'Saran' presentation machine
6232	BE2d	Richthofen's 26th victim 11.3.1917. Replica built by RAF
6259	BE2e	Fitted 75hp Rolls Royce Hawk and tested by RNAS at Cranwell
B2312	Camel	Tested at Farnborough with self-sealing fuel tanks Feb. 1920
B5648	Camel	Aircraft in which Lt. Alan Jerrard won his V.C.
B7320	Camel	70 Sq. Lt. Todd's aircraft
B7380	Camel	Rustons 1000th aircraft 4.1.1918
D1922	Camel	'Residents in Siam No.2' presentation machine
D1963	Camel	One of the last flying. Farnborough April 1923

AIRCRAFT BUILT BY ROBEY & CO. GLOBE WORKS LINCOLN 1915-1919

(in serial number order)

SERIAL NOS	QUANTITY	TYPE	REMARKS
3833-3862	30	Sopwith 806 Gunbus	21.5.1915. 150hp Sunbeam Nubian 3850-62 d/d as spares
9041-9060	20	Short 184	23.11.1915. 225hp Sunbeam Mohawk 9041-9046
			240hp Sunbeam Gurkha 9047-9060
9498-9499	2	Robey Peters Fighting Machine	17.4.1916. 250hp Rolls Royce V12
N33-35	3	Robey Seaplane	16.4.1917. 200hp Hispano Suiza cancelled
N1220-1229	10	Short 184 improved type	1.2.1917. 240hp Sunbeam Gurkha
N1260-1279	20	Short 184 improved type	30.12.1916. 225hp Sunbeam Mohawk N1274 Renault
N1820-1839	20	Short 184 modified	17.4.1917. 240hp Renault N1827-39 Sunbeam Maori
N2820-2849	30	Short 184 Dover type	25.10.1917. 260hp Sunbeam Maori
N2900-2949	50	Short 184	26.11.1917. 260hp Sunbeam Maori
N5000-5029	30	Maurice Farman S.7	10.5.1916. 75hp Rolls Royce Hawk N5017-29 cancelled
N9000-9059	60	Short 184	260hp Sunbeam Maori N9000 d/d 25.7.1918
N9140-9169	30	Short 184	11.4.1918. 260hp Sunbeam Maori
N9290-9349	60	Short 184	9.9.1918. Last 45 cancelled 14.1.1919

AIRCRAFT BUILT BY CLAYTON & SHUTTLEWORTH LIMITED 1916-1919

(in serial number order)

SERIAL NOS	QUANTITY	TYPE	REMARKS
A9813-9918	106	Sopwith Triplane	Cancelled
B5651-5750	100	Sopwith 1F1 Camel	
B7181-7280	100	Sopwith 1F1 Camel	
D3326-3425	100	Sopwith 1F1 Camel	
D9581-9680	100	Sopwith 1F1 Camel	
D9681-9730	50	Handley Page 0/400	Last four cancelled
E4374-4423	50	Sopwith 1F1 Camel	
F2996-3095	100	Vickers Vimy	Three delivered, balance cancelled
F3096-3145	50	Sopwith 1F1 Camel	
F4974-5073	100	Sopwith 1F1 Camel	Up to F5020 delivery confirmed
J251-300	50	Vickers Vimy	Cancelled
N533-538	6	Sopwith Triplane	
N541-543	3	Sopwith Triplane	
N5350-5389	40	Sopwith Triplane	
N8180-8229	50	Sopwith 2F1 Camel	Delivery up to N8204 confirmed

NOTES ON INDIVIDUAL MACHINES

SERIAL NOS	TYPE	REMARKS
B5710/1/45/7/8	Sopwith Camel	To Belgian government. B5747 preserved as SC-11, Belgian Air Force
B5713	Sopwith Camel	Two seat conversion
B7235/7	Sopwith Camel	To Belgian government
B7244	Sopwith Camel	Two seat conversion
N5384/7	Sopwith Triplane	Transferred to French government
N5388	Sopwith Triplane	Loaned to French

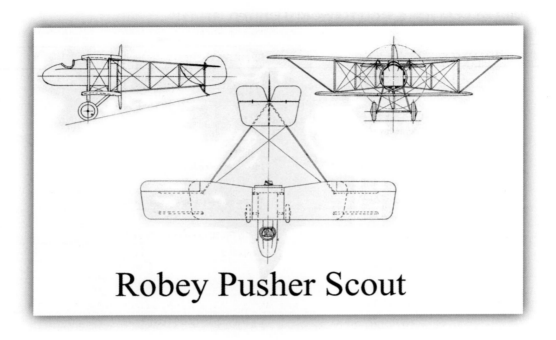

Robey Pusher Scout

ROBEY PUSHER SCOUT - 1915

DETAILS

Wingspan:	32' 5" (upper)	20' 0" (lower)
Engine:	80hp Gnome	90hp Salmson M7
Length:	23' 3½"	21' 11"
Weight empty:	760lb	980lb
Weight loaded:	1150lb	1370lb
Estimated max. speed:	82mph	93mph
Estimated climb:	1000ft/min	970ft/min

Robey Peters Fighting Machine - First Machine

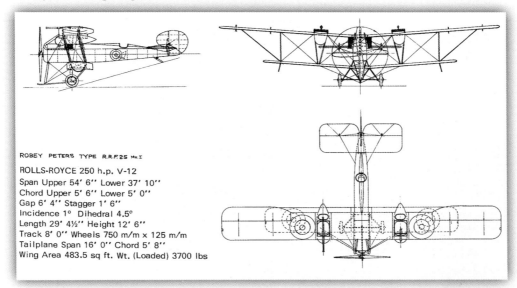

ROBEY PETERS TYPE R.R.F.25 Mk.I

ROLLS-ROYCE 250 h.p. V-12
Span Upper 54′ 6′′ Lower 37′ 10′′
Chord Upper 5′ 6′′ Lower 5′ 0′′
Gap 6′ 4′′ Stagger 1′ 6′′
Incidence 1° Dihedral 4.5°
Length 29′ 4½′′ Height 12′ 6′′
Track 8′ 0′′ Wheels 750 m/m x 125 m/m
Tailplane Span 16′ 0′′ Chord 5′ 8′′
Wing Area 483.5 sq ft. Wt. (Loaded) 3700 lbs

Robey Peters Fighting Machine - Second Machine

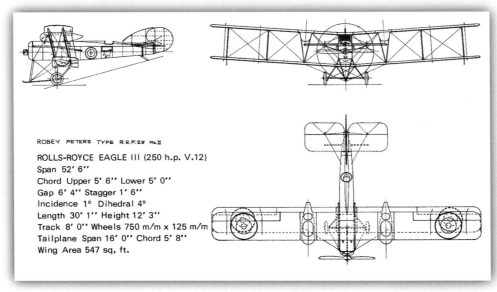

ROBEY PETERS TYPE R.R.F.25 Mk.II

ROLLS-ROYCE EAGLE III (250 h.p. V.12)
Span 52′ 6′′
Chord Upper 5′ 6′′ Lower 5′ 0′′
Gap 6′ 4′′ Stagger 1′ 6′′
Incidence 1° Dihedral 4°
Length 30′ 1′′ Height 12′ 3′′
Track 8′ 0′′ Wheels 750 m/m x 125 m/m
Tailplane Span 16′ 0′′ Chord 5′ 8′′
Wing Area 547 sq, ft.

ROBEY TRACTOR SCOUT BIPLANE - 1915

Estimated dimensions

DETAILS

Wingspan:	Approx. 24' 6"
Length:	Approx. 17' 8"
Height:	Approx. 8' 6"

ROBEY SEAPLANE TYPE HBS2

Single Seat shipboard floatplane class N1B

DETAILS

Wingspan:	Approx. 33'
Length:	27' 9½"
Height:	12' 0"

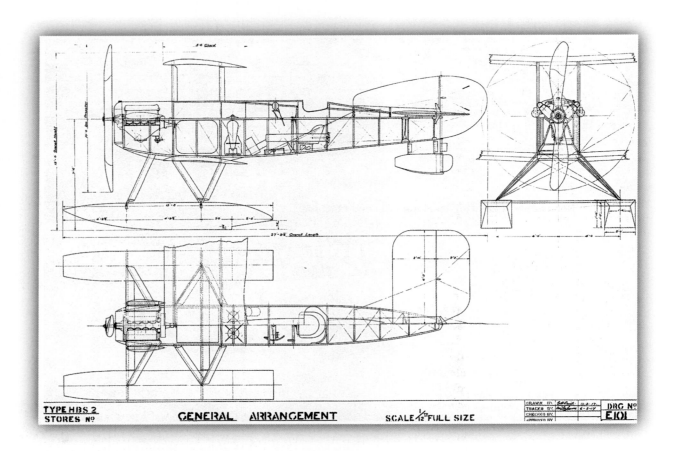

TYPE HBS 2
STORES Nº

GENERAL ARRANGEMENT

SCALE 1/12 FULL SIZE

DRG Nº
E101

NO.4
AIRCRAFT
ACCEPTANCE PARK

The West Common, like several other racecourses, was pressed into military use and became No. 4 Aircraft Acceptance Park in 1915. Aircraft were brought in sections by road from the manufacturers for completion and test flying before being accepted for service. Initially it had two landing strips turfed, 150 yards by 20 yards, and later, a 250 yard diameter landing circle bordered by lime was laid out. The original hangarage consisted of two triangular roofed, camouflaged sheds situated at the clubhouse corner of the Common (the site of the present tennis courts) with openings facing the City Hospital. These were later supplemented by two sheds alongside Alderman's Walk, with doors at the ends. Ultimately they were converted into one large shed when the gap between them was roofed in. Later in the war, five Bessoneau sheds (canvas covered) were added, one opposite the grandstand and four (including two of extra height to house Handley Page and Blackburn bombers with folded wings) at the end of West Parade. The racecourse buildings were used for accommodation.

The Common was used to test all of the Ruston built aircraft plus Robey-built Sopwith Gunbus machines and, later, Bristol F2Bs built by Marshall of Gainsborough and Handley Page 0/400s built by Clayton and Shuttleworth. Various other machines built outside the county were also tested including the DH5, DH6, DH9, Sopwith Cuckoo and Blackburn Kangaroo types.

⊙ *Two views of Ruston built Sopwith Camel B2359 early in September*
⊙ *1917 by the landing circle line (Norman Franks)*

The sheds were dismantled after the war and disposed of at local sales. The two original sheds became garages in Lincoln; one, Gilberts in Pelham Street and the other, Stocks in Lucy Tower Street. Both survived into the 1960s.

The Common had houses on one side and it sloped steeply from the East so it was not an ideal airfield. J.H. Moore, one of the early test pilots, commented that he shuddered at the thought of landing an aircraft on such a spot. *"The prevailing wind generally meant that you had to land parallel with Alderman's Walk, and as the ground was dropping away all the time it was a bit tricky."*

When Robey & Co. received a second contract from the Admiralty for Maurice Farman MF7 Longhorn trainers in May 1916 they decided to establish their own test airfield. The Ecclesiastical Commissioners were approached and a piece of land next to the Mental Hospital at Bracebridge Heath was acquired. A wooden shed with a large sign 'Robeys Aerodrome' on the front, was erected on the north side of the site adjacent to the wall of the hospital cemetery. The airfield was also used for the testing of the Robey-Peters fighting machines and Sopwith Triplanes and Camels built by Clayton & Shuttleworth Ltd.

The War Office decided to develop Robey's Aerodrome to replace the West Common and later in 1916 the airfield was taken over and enlarged with 10 canvas Bessoneau hangars at the south end near St John's Farm. It was placed under the Technical Wing of the Midlands Area as an Aircraft Acceptance Park for Handley Page and 'ordinary' aircraft plus delivery work by air. It was also to be used for the storage of aircraft. There was a proposal to build two large erection shops, each 540 ft x 70 ft, on the north side of the airfield for the Handley Page 0/400 bombers contracted to Clayton & Shuttleworth; however there is no evidence to suggest that any work on these took place.

In the latter part of 1917 further work commenced to turn the site into a permanent airfield for the Royal Flying Corps (RAF from 1st April 1918) and seven brick hangars with Belfast-truss roofs were constructed and accommodation was built to the west of Sleaford Road.

In August 1918 No.120 Squadron moved in to Bracebridge Heath from Cramlington to commence training for the Independent Air Force. The squadron began to re-equip with DH9 bombers in October, however the Armistice in November ended the need for new squadrons for the Western Front and it moved out a month later and subsequently disbanded without ever becoming fully operational. Another light bomber unit, No.121 Squadron, reformed at Bracebridge Heath on 14th October 1918. It was scheduled to operate twin-engined DH10 'Amiens' bombers from 1st December 1918, but this proposal was also abandoned before any aircraft were delivered.

The Aircraft Acceptance Park did not complete its move from the Common until 1919 and it closed the following year. The landing ground reverted to agriculture and the temporary hangars were dismantled and sold off. Most of the camp was cleared but a small number of bungalows were left on the west side of Sleaford Road. Some of the accommodation huts were bought by local people and re-erected in the surrounding area and eighty years later some of these are still in use. Between the wars, buildings on the main site were leased to a number of private companies including Lincolnshire Road Car Co.

⊕ *Royal Flying Corps crest in the racecourse grandstand*